MY FIRST LEARNING SE...

TIME

M000035534

Written and Illustrated by Caroline and John Astrop

Text and illustrations ©1993 by Caroline and John Astrop.
Originally published by Regency House Limited.

Modern Publishing
A Division of Unisystems, Inc./New York, New York 10022
Printed in the U.S.A.

7 o'clock
Ted quickly jumps out of bed.
Do you get up at 7 o'clock?

Which animals are fast and which are slow?

8 o'clock
Ted has cereal for breakfast.
What do you like for breakfast?

Find the right breakfast for each friend.

9 o'clock
Ted rides his tricycle.
How many flowers can you see?

10 o'clock
Time to clean up Ted's room.
Is your room neat?

11 o'clock
Ted helps Dad in the garden.
What is Dad doing?

Help Sam Snail find his way out of the garden.

12:00

12 o'clock
Ted has lunch with the toys.
What do you think these toys' names are?

1 o'clock
Tired Ted takes a nap.
Who else is asleep?

2 o'clock
Time to play.
How many friends does Ted have?

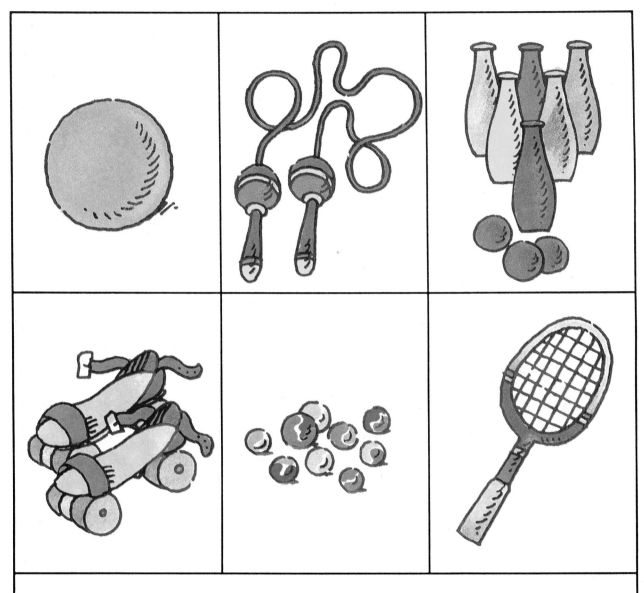

Can you say what these toys are?

3 o'clock
Off to the store with Mommy.
How is Ted helping his mother?

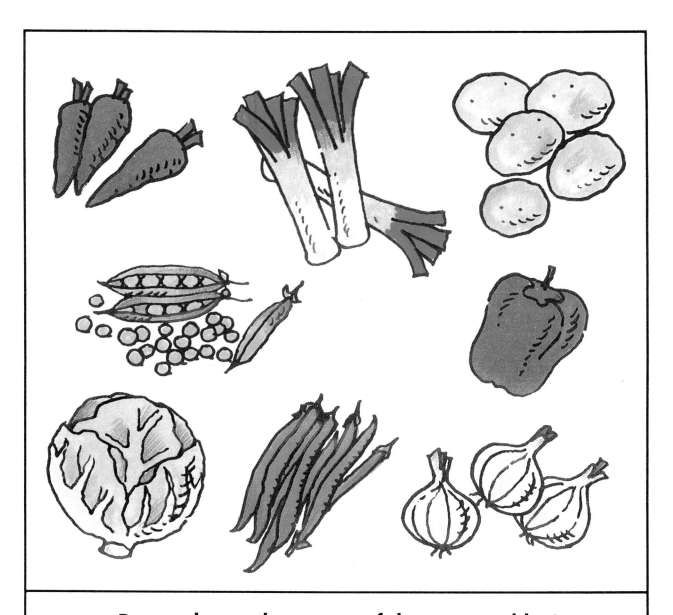

Do you know the names of these vegetables?

4 o'clock
Television time.
What is your favorite TV show?

Which clock does not say 4 o'clock?

5 o'clock
A picnic in the garden.
What does Ted like to eat?

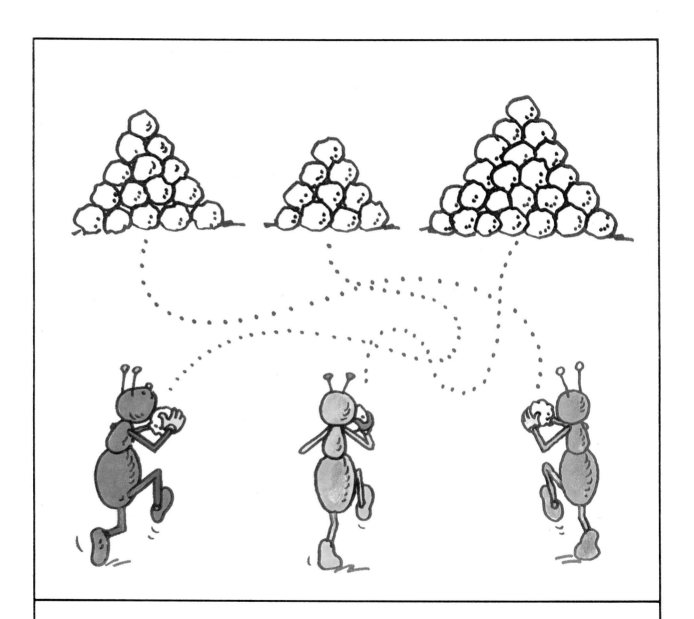

Which ant has collected the most crumbs?

6 o'clock
Time for a bath.
Can you blow bubbles?

7 o'clock
Ted is tucked up in bed.
Is he asleep yet?

Twelve different clocks.

Can you say the time on each one?

We hope you
enjoyed learning
about

TIME